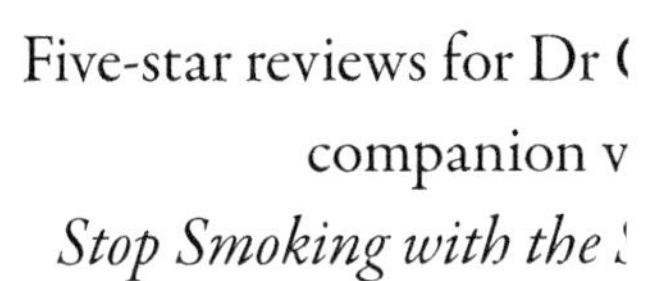

Empowering. Simple succinct and makes total sense very grateful for this informative read. It's like the simplest secret and it makes a previously seemingly impossible task feel totally achievable. Thank you Dr S.

(K. Forde, United Kingdom)

Very interesting read definitely gives you a different perspective on the thought process about how to quit smoking ... and buying it on kindle costs about as much as a pack of cigarettes... buy this book read this book spread the word!

(Kelly, United States)

You need to be ready to quit, that's really part one to the whole process. I have not smoked another cigarette since I read the last page of the e-book and it's been six weeks and I'm still going strong. I recommend writing yourself some notes to look at when you start having some issues; I was concerned I couldn't bookmark what I needed to look at quick enough. Everything this short book says is true, and IT WORKED FOR ME -- smoked a pack a day for 25 years and I QUIT. It's amazing.

(James A. Gee, United States)

Simple, effective, worth the buy. It's not a miracle solution, it's actually just a very simple method to change the way you think about your nicotine addiction. It worked for me, been off the JUUL for well over a month at this point.

(Carson Bartholomew, United States)

It actually helped. Wish I would have stuck with it!

(C.M., United States)

Stop Vaping with the Symonds Method

BY THE SAME AUTHOR

Stop Smoking: Real Help at Last

Smoking is a Psychological Problem

Stop Smoking with the Symonds Method

Midlife: Problems and Solutions (Editor)

Shmoogie: A Dispute Between Brothers

An English Doctor in Japan

Stop Vaping with the Symonds Method

How to become nicotine-free for life

Dr Gabriel Symonds

YOUCAXTON PUBLICATIONS
OXFORD AND SHREWSBURY

ISBN 978-1-914424-24-3
Published by YouCaxton Publications 2021
YCBN: 01

YouCaxton Publications
www.youcaxton.co.uk

Contents

Introduction

The Symonds Method

Introduction

Why you need this book

This book is intended for vapers who wish to stop vaping and all nicotine use but find it difficult and are looking for help.

Or maybe you're unsure about whether to stop vaping. Of course you're unsure – that's why you vape! What is the source of this uncertainty? On common-sense grounds it's not going to do you any good to inhale nicotine together with many other chemicals repeatedly every day for years on end.

That said, I shall not try to persuade you that you *ought* to stop vaping, but for those who may be in doubt, I hope to show that becoming nicotine-free is much easier than you think.

The hesitation and doubt arise because the prospect of never vaping (or using some other form of nicotine) again may seem intolerable. Indeed, most people start vaping in the first place as a replacement for smoking. But now they're afraid to stop.

I hasten to say that the Symonds Method is nothing to do with scare tactics, hypnosis, or gimmicks of any kind.

On the contrary, this book sets out to help you *demonstrate to yourself* how you can develop a new attitude to vaping such that you won't want to do it anymore. So you won't.

The interactive approach presented here is straight-forward and can be completed in one or two sittings. It's a companion volume to my book, *Stop Smoking with the Symonds Method: All you need to know to stop smoking easily,* which has helped many smokers to become non-smokers again.

What is the success rate of the Symonds Method?

Vaping is a voluntary activity, though the urge to keep puffing on your e-cigarette may be hard to resist. The concept of success rate, therefore, is something of an artificial problem.

For example, if someone stops vaping with the help of the Symonds Method for a year, and then, quite voluntarily, decides to start vaping again, does this mean my method has failed? No, it means the vaper has changed his or her mind about being nicotine-free and wish to be a nicotine-user again.

What I can say is that, in my experience, 80 per cent of people stop nicotine use after coming to see me once; a further 10 per cent of the total stop after a second visit and are nicotine-free when followed-up a month later.

Stopping nicotine use, however, is the easy bit.

The real challenge is *staying stopped* and how to do this is explained in detail below.

Once this is understood, it should be possible for all vapers, without a struggle, to return permanently to the normal state of being *nicotine-free*.

What are e-cigarettes?

E-cigarettes (electronic cigarettes) are devices that simulate cigarette smoking.

They consist of a cartridge or tank containing a liquid (variously called vape juice, e-juice, or e-liquid) which is heated by a battery-powered coil to produce a nicotine-laced aerosol which is inhaled through the mouthpiece.

E-cigarettes come in a variety of shapes and sizes, as shown:

The word 'vaping' and related words 'to vape', 'vapes', etc., are commonly used to mean inhaling (breathing in, or sucking into your lungs) the aerosol produced by an e-cigarette.

The word 'vapour' (vapor in the US) is inaccurately used for what can be seen, the 'cloud' or 'mist' that is breathed out when someone is using an e-cigarette. Vapour is a gas, such as water vapour that you can see coming out of a kettle on the boil or from a domestic humidifier, but an aerosol means a suspension of tiny particles of liquid or solid, or both, within a gas.

It's important to know this because the vapour, so called, consists of many substances suspended in the aerosol, as in the following illustration:

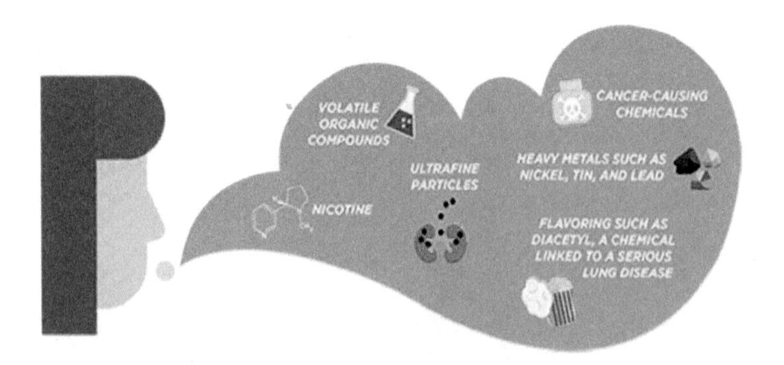

The actual composition of the aerosol varies by brand, but besides nicotine it commonly contains propylene glycol, vegetable glycerin, synthetic flavours, tobacco-specific nitrosamines, aldehydes, metal nanoparticles, volatile organic compounds, and trace amounts of other toxicants and carcinogens.

The main ingredient that produces the aerosol is propylene glycol. This chemical is widely used as a food additive, as an ingredient in many cosmetic and hygiene products, to make polyester fibers, and to generate theatre 'fog'. In the reassuring words of the US Food and Drug Administration, propylene glycol is 'generally recognized as safe.'

This means it's believed to be safe when *eaten* or applied to the skin, but these are entirely different situations from when it's *inhaled*.

The same considerations apply to the flavours. More then 7,000 are available, including those which are attractive to children and teenagers, such as chocolate raspberry, cherry cheesecake, cotton candy, vanilla, grape, apple, coffee, bubble gum, etc.

The concentration of nicotine in e-cigarette liquid varies from none (nicotine-free) up to 36 mg/ml or even more. Common concentrations are 6 mg/ml, 12 mg/ml, 18 mg/ml, or 24 mg/ml.

Some e-cigarettes use nicotine salts produced by combining nicotine with an *acid*, such as lactic, benzoic, levulinic, salicyclic, malic, or tartaric acid.

Do you really want to put this into your lungs?

'Heat-not-burn' tobacco products

In the last few years so-called heat-not-burn devices for inhaling tobacco fumes have become available as an alternative to smoking. They go under different names (some unpronounceable) according to the manufacturer, for example, 'IQOS' (Philip Morris), 'glo' (British American Tobacco), and 'Ploom' (Japan Tobacco International).

These products are heavily advertised in a drive to persuade smokers that they are safer than combustible cigarettes. So far this has not proved to be the case, nor would one expect it to be. Studies have found that they contain levels of nicotine and carcinogens comparable to conventional cigarettes.

If you use one of these products you'll probably be exposed to risks similar to those of smoking, and you'll have the same problem of stopping them due to nicotine addiction.

Vaping in children

Apart from the majority who use vaping to help them quit smoking, children may take up vaping because their friends are doing it, or they try it from curiosity, or because they think it looks cool.

The result, as with those who switched from smoking, is that many of them continue vaping for years on end because *they find themselves unable to stop.*

A common way children get into this unfortunate situation, especially in America, is through a type of e-cigarette which goes by the catchy name of JUUL. It's a discrete device that looks like a USB stick but it contains a relatively high concentration of nicotine so it's easy to become addicted to it.

There was a report in *Wired Magazine* (23 July 2018) that at least three customers had filed complaints against JUUL. They allege that 'JUUL deceptively marketed the product as safe, when it contains more potent doses of nicotine than cigarettes.'

The report continues: 'One complainant claims he became addicted to nicotine salts in the JUUL pods of which he now uses several each week, and another says he purchased JUUL to help him quit smoking but "the intense dosage of nicotine salts delivered by the JUUL products resulted in an increased nicotine addiction, and an increased consumption of nicotine."'

This is bad enough, but a third complainant, the mother of a fifteen-year-old, alleged that 'JUUL designed its product to contain more nicotine than necessary to satisfy the cravings of an adult smoker,' and that her child 'became heavily addicted to nicotine, making him "anxious, highly irritable and prone to angry outbursts," and perform poorly in school.'

Of course this poor child is anxious, highly irritable, prone to angry outbursts, and performing poorly in school as a result of using JUUL. These are nicotine withdrawal symptoms which, on top of all the normal pressures and demands of schooling, no child should have to deal with.

What are our lungs for?

The function of the lungs is gaseous exchange. This happens in the deepest recesses of the lungs, called the alveoli, and means that oxygen in inhaled air is passed into the bloodstream, and carbon dioxide, a waste product of metabolism, passes from the bloodstream into the lungs to be exhaled (breathed out) into the air.

It's a beautiful sophisticated system that works constantly to keep us alive.

What our lungs are *not* intended for is the absorption of addictive drugs or tobacco fumes, and it's obvious that if you repeatedly inhale anything other than clean air you may damage your health.

(Exceptions are the gases used in general anaesthesia and inhalers for the treatment of asthma.)

Vaping and smoking compared

Vaping is unlike smoking in one important aspect: it's clear when a cigarette is finished. But with vaping, on the other hand, the supply of nicotine is continuous for as long as you keep pressing on the button to activate the release of the vapour (until the supply of e-juice runs out).

Here is a description of one person's use of e-cigarettes (slightly paraphrased):

> Three years after puffing my first e-cig I was vaping *all the goddamn time*. All night when I'm out with friends and now all day while I'm at work...But if a project is particularly stressful (or just slightly vexatious – any excuse will do), my sleek little e-cig is sitting in my bag at my feet. Maybe just one puff. Maybe one more. Like a never-ending pipe, you don't know when you've had enough, unlike when you've had a cigarette's worth of nicotine. One quick puff to slay your stress can turn into one puff every few minutes, and then whenever I get the slightest urge...E-cigarettes, in all their stylish sneakiness, have taken over my life...The way to quit smoking isn't through a device that makes a nicotine hit easier, or fun. I have to learn to hate it. (Emphasis in original.)[1]

---

[1] https://www.menshealth.com/health/a23937726/vaping-vs-smoking/

My own research shows similar results. One vaper said, 'For me it's around 100 puffs a day, though this can be much more if I'm not busy or am having a few beers.' Another told me he couldn't put a figure on how many puffs he used but noted, 'I constantly seem to have the vape in my hand, so I suppose I vape continually.'

The variation in vaping patterns between individuals may be considerable and depends on how much nicotine they feel they need. This is affected by the depth of inhalations of the aerosol and the length of time they hold it in their lungs before breathing out.

Some aspects of vaping behaviour mimic those of smoking: the hand-to-mouth gesture, the feeling of the vapour being drawn into the mouth, and the spectacle of it being exhaled. But these are also the very aspects that will make smokers who switch to vaping *keep doing it*, perhaps with periodic lapses back to smoking.

Not only that, but the vaper has the inconvenience and expense of buying regular supplies of e-liquid, keeping the device charged up, and always remembering to take it with him or her on leaving home. And this may well continue *for the rest of the person's life*.

Is nicotine addictive?

The obvious answer is yes.

A concise definition of addiction is to be found in the *Shorter Oxford English Dictionary:* 'The state of dependence on a drug to the extent that it cannot be withdrawn without adverse effects.' This sufficiently covers the situation with nicotine. The vast majority of those who use this chemical feel a compulsion to dose themselves with it at frequent intervals, because if they don't, they experience withdrawal symptoms, mild though these are. (Some people claim to suffer severe effects if this drug is withdrawn, which I'll discuss later.)

Nonetheless, there are some, whom one might call nicotine addiction deniers, who claim nicotine is not addictive because no obvious direct harm results from its use, in contrast with, say, heroin. Or they may say it's no more addictive than caffeine or sugar, or that it's impossible to make someone addicted to pure nicotine if they have not previously been a smoker or vaper. This suggests there is something in cigarette smoke or in the e-cigarette aerosol which, in combination with nicotine, is what causes the addiction; or that it's the rapidity with which nicotine is transferred into the bloodstream and thence to the brain as happens with smoking and vaping that accounts for the addictiveness of these two ways of putting nicotine into your body.

Such arguments are sometimes used in support of the claim that nicotine itself is harmless and therefore it doesn't matter if one goes merrily vaping away for the rest of one's life. Indeed, there are some vapers who claim they are quite happy sucking a nicotine-laced aerosol into their lungs hundreds of times every day and they don't want to stop. Or some may say they only use it for a particular purpose, such as when needing to concentrate on writing a report, or on some special occasion.

There are also those who try to argue in defence of nicotine by pointing out studies which claim to show that nicotine is a cognitive enhancer (increases alertness and augments memory), may reduce the risk of dementia, and that it has a beneficial effect in ulcerative colitis (inflammation of the large bowel).

If one looks into these studies, however, they are either experimental or the results are provisional and in need of replication, or they are written as opinion pieces; they are usually to be found in obscure online journals. Nonetheless, although it's possible that one day nicotine might be found to have a place in medical practice, at present, apart from the dubious use of nicotine to treat nicotine addiction, it's not recommended for the prevention or treatment of any disease.

Once a nicotine addict, always a nicotine addict?

To talk of vaping as a means of quitting smoking is disingenuous if not misleading.

If someone switches completely from smoking cigarettes to vaping, in a literal sense they can be said to have quit smoking – but they're still putting nicotine into their body, and are likely to go on putting nicotine into their body for months, years, or even the rest of their lives.

The suggestion or advice to turn to vaping as an allegedly less harmful alternative to smoking is *a counsel of despair and almost an insult* to smokers. It implies 'once a nicotine addict, always a nicotine addict.'

Furthermore, it colludes with smokers that quitting unaided is too difficult, and thus provides a ready excuse to *carry on* smoking, or at least to carry on using nicotine in some or other alternative way.

Vaping is an example of the so-called harm-reduction approach.

This flawed concept is patronising and defeatist; it amounts to saying:

> Never mind, you poor smoker. We understand. Quitting is too difficult, so why don't you at least think about trying to continue using nicotine in a way which is (probably) less harmful?

Such a wrong-headed notion stems from inability or unwillingness to see smoking for what it is: *legalised drug (nicotine) addiction*. The implication is that nicotine addicts are stuck with it: they'll never be able to return to the happy state (other things being equal) they were in before they took up smoking, and become nicotine-free again.

Even if – and it's a big if – a smoker manages to switch from inhaling poisonous tobacco fumes to inhaling a (probably) less poisonous nicotine-laced aerosol, what does this mean in practice?

A study[2] published in November 2020 of 100 e-cigarette users in the US who were former smokers, found that on average they took 365 puffs per day; one third of this number vaped within five minutes of waking in the morning, and 56 per cent vaped throughout the day.

If we assume a vaper sleeps for eight hours, spends two hours eating, and two hours in non-vaping environments, that leaves twelve hours or 720 minutes free for vaping, which means, for the majority of vapers in this study, one puff or inhalation every two minutes. Thus, *the vaping device hardly ever leaves their hand.*

Whatever the number of puffs that vapers inhale each day, they feel repeated urges to take another dose of their nicotine aerosol wherever they happen to be. If they're outside it's difficult to defer the need to satisfy the urge until they get home and can do it in private.

---

[2] https://doi.org/10.18332/tid/128319

In other words, they're almost constantly or repeatedly suffering low-level nicotine withdrawal symptoms which the e-cigarette doesn't quite relieve, or if it does relieve the symptoms it's only short-lived and then they want another puff! Worse, the vaper is probably longing for a drag on a real cigarette, with its rich aroma and satisfying flavour derived from the tar, nicotine, and thousands of other chemicals in the tobacco fumes as they are breathed deeply into the lungs.

Vapers, however, will put up with the state of mild discomfort and frustration because Public Health England (see below) has said e-cigarettes are 95 per cent safer than smoking! And for the sake of their health they *must not* go back to smoking, though many of them do, on and off if not completely (dual use).

Now we can see why the largely unregulated e-cigarette industry – a multi-billion dollar global enterprise – is so involved in promoting thousands of wondrous flavours in their products: it gives an ostensible reason for vapers who were former smokers to *keep vaping!*

By this means vapers are manipulated into believing they vape to experience the joys of the flavours, because these may compensate, to a small extent anyway, for the lack of the full satisfaction they previously believed they obtained from smoking cigarettes. Otherwise, why not use a nicotine inhaler? There is one brand of such a product, called Nicotrol.

Here is a repetitively written extract from what one drug database has to say about this device:

> The Nicotrol inhaler provides the smoker with adequate amounts of nicotine to reduce the urge to smoke, and *may provide some degree of comfort* by providing a hand-to-mouth ritual similar to smoking, although the importance of such an effect in smoking cessation is, as yet, unknown. (Emphasis added.)

Why do smokers desirous of quitting need the *comfort* of a hand-to-mouth ritual?

Vaping is 95 per cent safer than smoking – or is it?

Vaping enthusiasts are fond of saying that vaping is 95 per cent safer than smoking. Indeed, this nice round figure is quoted so often that it's almost become a mantra. How did such a claim arise? It's quite a saga. Let's take a look.

The 95 per cent figure first appeared in an online journal called *European Addiction Research* in April 2014.[3] Twelve people are listed as authors, the first of whom is the well-named and eccentric Professor David Nutt, a neuropsychopharmacologist, no less. The paper was called *Estimating the Harms of Nicotine-Containing Products Using the MCDA Approach* (MCDA means multi-criteria decision

[3] https://www.karger.com/article/fulltext/360220

analysis) and was produced as a result of a weekend workshop held in London in July 2013. The participants used a complicated statistical formula and theoretical criteria whereby, somehow, if ordinary cigarettes are regarded as 100 per cent harmful, e-cigarettes were calculated to be only about 5 per cent as harmful.

The conclusion of the weekend deliberation was:

> Cigarettes are the nicotine product causing by far the most harm to users and others in the world today. Attempts to switch to non-combusted sources of nicotine should be encouraged as the harms from these products are much lower.

The first sentence is undoubtedly true. However, the claim in the second sentence – that the harms from non-combusted sources of nicotine are much lower than cigarettes – although plausible, is merely an assumption. But even if it were true, it does not necessarily follow that 'attempts to switch [to e-cigarettes] should be encouraged.'

In any case, why 'should' smokers be encouraged merely to attempt to switch to e-cigarettes? Instead of aiming so low, why not encourage smokers to quit smoking and all nicotine use? As I explain in my book, *Stop Smoking with the Symonds Method,* this is not nearly as difficult as it may seem.

Before getting carried away, as so many have done, with the 95 per cent figure, it would be as well to take note of the cautions expressed in the original paper (emphases added):

- *Our understanding of the potential hazards associated with using electronic nicotine delivery systems (e-cigarettes) is at a very early stage*
- A limitation of this study is the lack of hard evidence for the harms of most products on most of the criteria
- Another weakness might be the kind of sample of experts. There was no formal criterion for the recruitment of the experts
- The results of this study *suggest* that of all nicotine-containing products, cigarettes (and small cigars in the USA) are very much the most harmful

Subsequently, the workshop's conclusion was quoted approvingly in a report issued in 2015 by Public Health England (PHE) called *E-cigarettes: an evidence update*, and used by PHE to promote these nicotine delivery devices for smoking cessation. The lead author was one Ann McNeill who, in these days of super-specialization, is a Professor of Tobacco Addiction in the National Addiction Centre. We'll come back to her in a moment.

Another author was the clinical psychologist Professor Peter Hajek, who is on record as saying that 'nicotine itself is probably safer than caffeine,' and though he denies links with any e-cigarette manufacturer, has received research funding from and provided consultancy to manufacturers of so-called stop-smoking medications.

The PHE report, however, was strongly criticized in an editorial in the prestigious medical journal, *The Lancet,*[4] which pointed out that the report's conclusions were based on a study of 'the opinions of a small group of individuals with no pre-specified expertise in tobacco control.' Oh dear.

Furthermore, two of the portly Professor Nutt's colleagues are mentioned in *The Lancet* editorial as having potential conflicts of interest due to their associations with an e-cigarette distributor and manufacturers of smoking cessation products, respectively. Oh dear again.

Incidentally, Professor Nutt in 2009 was dismissed as chair of the UK government's Advisory Council on the Misuse of Drugs after saying that ecstasy, cannabis, and LSD are less dangerous than alcohol and tobacco.

The British Medical Journal also weighed in with an aptly titled article, *Evidence about electronic cigarettes: a foundation built on rock or sand?*[5] The authors point out a number of potential serious problems with e-cigarettes, among which are (paraphrased):

[4] https://www.thelancet.com/journals/lancet/article/PIIS0140-6736(15)00042-2/fulltext
[5] BMJ 2015;351:h4863

- Children and adolescents may take up e-cigarettes and progress to smoking
- The long-term effects of e-cigarettes are unknown
- E-cigarette liquids contain formaldehyde as well as flavourings and other substances which may be harmful to health
- If e-cigarettes are used to reduce smoking, as opposed to quitting, there may be no overall benefit for health
- There is no evidence that e-cigarettes are effective as aids for quitting smoking
- There may be a risk to bystanders from second-hand vaping in enclosed public places

Of course, Professor Ann McNeill was not going to take this lying down. She became very cross at all this criticism of her 'e-cigarettes are at least 95 per cent less harmful than tobacco' claim, especially at *The British Medical Journal* article which she called offensive.

Another person in what I call the Tobacco Control Lobby, who also gets a bit carried away, is the self-styled world expert on smoking and addiction, Professor Robert West. He's a psychiatrist who is on record as saying: 'If we fail to take this opportunity that electronic cigarettes are potentially providing then we're really condemning [smokers] to death.'[6]

[6] https://www.youtube.com/watch?v=_cqgbdfZk20&t=22s

Condemning smokers to death? Do we line them up against a wall or string them up from lamp-posts? What I guess he means is that if we (whoever 'we' are) fail to take this opportunity, etc., then you, the smoker, are going to die because e-cigarettes are not available because of unprogressive legislation or because it was believed they were dangerous when they weren't.

What a strange idea. Because we don't all rush to embrace e-cigarettes, many unfortunates who are suffering from the incurable disease of smoking will die. But all they have to do, to avoid an untimely death from this cause, is to *stop smoking* (unless they've left it too late, of course).

The PHE report concludes: 'It would be preferable for a young person to use an e-cigarette instead of smoking.'

How about not using nicotine at all, in any form?

Harm reduction or harm replacement?

Vaping is promoted in some quarters, particularly in Britain, as a so-called harm reduction approach for smokers who 'can't or don't want to stop smoking.' Putting it like that shows an unfortunate lack of understanding about why smokers really smoke and why they *seem* to be unable to stop.

All smokers can't or don't want to stop smoking—that's why they smoke! Or at least they think they can't stop, and that's why they may say, if asked, that they don't *want* to stop.

One of the main objections to vaping as a way of stopping smoking is that it reinforces the widely held but mistaken idea that stopping smoking is terribly, *terribly* difficult. So if you can't stop smoking then you can do something similar which appears to be less harmful.

You'll still have the hand-to-mouth gestures, the feeling of sucking something into your mouth, a mild form of the 'throat hit', and the image of yourself blowing out a cloud of smoke-like vapour from your mouth, or from your nose as well if you're really clever, which will enable you to look and feel like a smoker without smoking!

Indeed, there's a 2016 report by the UK Royal College of Physicians with the intriguing title, *Nicotine without smoke,* and the subtitle, *Tobacco harm reduction.* Roll up, roll up, ladies and gentlemen: now you can get your nicotine fixes in a less harmful way with ersatz smoking!

Even if vaping were not just 95 per cent safer than smoking but 100 per cent safe, what would be the point of doing it?

To avoid having to deal with stopping smoking, even if as a result you'll vape for the rest of your life?

To experience the joys of your taste buds being tickled by the flavoured aerosol passing over your tongue on its way down to the deepest recesses of your lungs?

Apart from those mentioned above, the many flavours available vary from rhubarb and custard to the charming-sounding unicorn vomit. (I kid you not: there is such a flavour available from a company which calls itself Vape Junkie E-Juice, with the entrancing subtitle, 'A Hard Habit To Break'. This particular company also sells e-juice flavours with more wholesome-sounding names, such as 'Orange Pineapple' though you can be certain that that particular flavour has never seen an orange or a pineapple in its life and is entirely synthetic.)

I must admit that on occasion I do eat rhubarb and custard, and, rather more frequently, oranges and pineapples. But there is a world of difference between *eating* these foods and *breathing the synthetic flavours into your lungs*.

In any case, how effective is vaping as a means of stopping smoking? The respected Cochrane Review posed the question: *Can electronic cigarettes help people stop smoking, and do they have any unwanted effects when used for this purpose?*

And the answer?

> For every 100 people using nicotine e-cigarettes to stop smoking, ten might successfully stop, compared with only six of 100 people using nicotine-replacement therapy or nicotine-free e-cigarettes, or four of 100 people having no support or behavioural support only.[7]

The unwanted effects most often reported with nicotine e-cigarettes were throat or mouth irritation, headache, cough, and feeling sick. These effects diminished over time as people continued using nicotine e-cigarettes.

Thus, 90 per cent of those using c-cigarettes to stop smoking failed, and unwanted effects were a problem for some of them.

Nonetheless, the 10 per cent of smokers who switch completely can feel complacent that with the approval of government health agencies they have 'stopped smoking'– even though, instead of inhaling tobacco fumes, they're puffing away on their e-cigarette nicotine delivery device hundreds of times every day!

In other words, vaping, as a means of quitting smoking, so called, merely defers the problem of stopping nicotine use.

---

[7] https://www.cochrane.org/CD010216/TOBACCO_can-electronic-cigarettes-help-people-stop-smoking-and-do-they-have-any-unwanted-effects-when-used (14 October 2020)

Why do vapers keep vaping?

Understanding this is the key to stopping vaping without tears.

If you switch to vaping in an attempt to quit smoking, and if you're successful, you'll then be facing three possibilities:

1. Carry on vaping for the foreseeable future – possibly even for the rest of your life.

2. Sooner later attempt to wean yourself off vaping and become nicotine-free.

In the second-mentioned, one way to do this is by gradually reducing the strength of nicotine in the vape juice so eventually you'll be down to 0 mg/ml ('zero nic'). Then you can just stop. Alternatively, you can carry on with a nicotine-free vape enjoying the hand-to-mouth gestures and the flavoured aerosol.

If you try to wean yourself off nicotine in this way you'll be no better off than attempting to quit smoking by gradually cutting down the number of cigarettes smoked each day. Such a strategy usually fails because the cutting down process can be stretched out indefinitely, and even if smokers do manage to reduce overall the number of cigarettes smoked daily, this will do very little to improve their health and the goal of becoming a non-smoker again without using an alternative source of nicotine will remain elusive.

Furthermore, if you gradually reduce the strength of nicotine in the e-liquid, you'll have the worst of both worlds: not allowing yourself to take as much nicotine as and when you feel you need it, so you'll be tempted to take deeper and more frequent inhalations to compensate; and being in a prolonged state of nicotine withdrawal.

This approach also reinforces the widely held but mistaken idea that stopping all nicotine use is extremely difficult. Thus, you'll have a new dilemma on your hands: either continue vaping indefinitely or struggle with nicotine withdrawal – the same problem that made you switch from smoking to vaping in the first place.

3. Stop vaping abruptly.

I shall attempt to show later in this book that 3. is the best and easiest way to become nicotine-free.

The expression 'cold turkey' is sometimes used for abrupt quitting: it implies using willpower to force yourself not to vape (or smoke) in spite of wanting to.

The Symonds Method, however, aims to show you how first to lose the desire to vape – and then stop.

After all, there should no difficulty in refraining from something you don't *want* to do anymore!

How to stop vaping

As I explain in my book on how to stop smoking, stopping vaping without a struggle depends on *understanding*. Understanding, that is, of two things:

1. Why you really vape, as opposed to why you think you vape, and

2. Why stopping vaping seems so hard.

In summary, the problem with both smoking and vaping is:

As long as you put nicotine into your body, you'll want to keep putting nicotine into your body.

Conventional approach to quitting nicotine

Insofar as you'll find any conventional advice on how to quit vaping, it will be similar to that recommended for quitting smoking.

Several steps are usually advised: these are unnecessary and, as I shall explain, counterproductive.

Prepare to quit and have a quit plan

What is there to prepare? It's not as if you're going to take an exam or the driving test. And what is there to plan?

You wish to be nicotine-free, but having to plan for this is discouraging – and if you fail you can blame it on having an inadequate plan.

Make a list of reasons why you want to quit

It's obvious: health and money, apart from other reasons. But you already know this – that's why you want to quit.

Choose a quit date

Bad idea. As a smoker or vaper your need is to quit *right now.* What's going to be different in ten days' or two weeks' time?

Choosing a quit date is merely a way of *putting off* the fateful day after which you are supposed never to put nicotine into your body again.

On the other hand, it may seem attractive because – let's face it – you don't really want to quit. Thus you can 'enjoy' the 'benefits' of nicotine for a little longer.

Work out how you'll cope with 'cravings'

So you'll have cravings (whatever these are) that will need to be coped with! Thanks very much. But is it true?

I hope that with the help of this book you'll demonstrate to yourself that such an idea is grossly exaggerated or plain wrong.

Quitting is a process or a journey

But it isn't. It's a state: either you smoke (or vape), or you don't.

Consider using prescription drugs

Very, *very* bad idea. As a vaper (or smoker) your brain is already in enough of an altered state with nicotine. What's the good of compounding this by using a drug which by design will cause a further disturbance in your brain's neurochemistry?

The two drugs in use for this dubious purpose are bupropion (Zyban) and varenicline (Champix, Chantix). Side effects are common and with varenicline they include suicidal thoughts!

The most important quitting resource of all

There is only one method or way of quitting nicotine that matters: YOURSELF.

You already have in you – in your intelligence and ability to think – the means of successful quitting.

And the key that will enable you to unlock this wonderful resource is *understanding*.

The Symonds Method

4 Steps

What follows is a reproduction in written form of what takes place in my face-to-face sessions that have proven so successful with hundreds of individual nicotine users.

The unique approach which I'll now show you is interactive and consists of four steps. These are colour-coded to key in with the corresponding parts of the text.

QUESTIONS. This is an information-gathering exercise to get a clear idea about why you are currently vaping.

UNDERSTANDING. You'll be shown how the answers to these questions will enable you *to demonstrate to yourself* the real reason you continue using nicotine.

INSTRUCTION. Keeping this understanding in mind, you'll be able to take the simple step needed to quit all nicotine use easily and permanently.

TIME TO START your nicotine-free life. The above three steps will show you why the best time to quit is *right now.*

How to use the Symonds Method

Although you might succeed in quitting vaping just by reading through this book, to get the best out of it, proceed as follows:

For the QUESTIONS part as below, please write down your answers in the spaces provided. If there isn't enough room (or if you prefer anyway), use a separate sheet of paper.

There are no right or wrong answers. Whatever you can think of is part of your experience of vaping and you'll see the importance of this as we progress.

Questions

1. **Why did you start vaping?**
   Answer:

2. **How many puffs on your e-cigarette do you take per day?**
   Answer:

3. **Why do you vape now? What is it like, or what effect does it have on you?**
   Answer:

4. **Why do you want to quit vaping?**
   Please make a list:

5. **What do you actually feel when you feel like taking a puff on your e-cigarette?**

This question is not as simple as it may seem, but it's the key to successful quitting. Try to write down as much as you can. If you can't think of anything, that's fine too, and if this applies in your case it's significant of itself.

It may help to imagine a scenario where you want to vape but aren't allowed to, such as being longer than expected on a flight or in a non-vaping and non-smoking meeting, or imagine you've run out of vape juice.

Many vapers will say they don't know what this would be like because they've never been in such a situation!

Nonetheless, it's important to try to remember *what you actually feel when you feel like puffing on your e-cigarette.*

You might even try an experiment: deliberately avoid vaping for a few hours (or longer if possible), and monitor how you feel as the time goes by.

Every hour write down exactly what you're feeling (if anything) and rate it on a scale of how bad (or mild) it is.

You might use a scale such as this:

0 – Don't notice anything
1 – Mild discomfort, easy to ignore
2 – Moderate discomfort, difficult to ignore
3 – Very troublesome symptoms
4 – Feel as if my head will explode!

It's important that you have written down your answers to the above questions before proceeding. The next page is left blank for your convenience.

Understanding

This section is the longest and will repay careful reading. Many people say they find it interesting and even enjoyable to follow.

You'll have your answers to the various questions written down.

Now we'll compare them with my suggested answers.

Typical answers

1. Why did you start vaping?

a) As a way of stopping smoking

or

b) I did not previously smoke cigarettes, but vaping seemed cool / I started out of curiosity / my friends were vaping / I wanted to blow clouds of vapour

It should be noted that both groups have the same problem: apparent inability to stop vaping.

2. How many puffs on your e-cigarette do you take per day?

a) About 100 / 200 / 300 / ...
b) Too many to count
c) I vape continually throughout the day
d) I don't know, but I vape from time to time whenever I feel like it

3. Why do you vape now? What is it like, or what effect does it have on you?

Your answer likely includes one of more of the following:

a) If I didn't vape I'd still be smoking!
b) I suppose it's just a habit
c) For the hand-to-mouth gestures
d) I'm only a social vaper / I only vape with a drink
e) Stress relief
f) Enjoyment
g) I love the taste and there are so many wonderful flavours to choose from!
h) Relieves boredom
i) Something to do with my hands
j) Lets me take a break
k) Helps concentration
l) Weight control
m) Blowing clouds of vapour is a cool new hobby
n) It's fun to vape with my friends

o) Nicotine addiction
p) It takes away the need to vape – until I want to do it again!

Next, we'll look at each of these in detail.

a) If I didn't vape I'd still be smoking!

This is the commonest reason for people to take up vaping. What it amounts to, as you are only too well aware, is that instead of smoking, say, twenty cigarettes every day, you're now taking hundreds of puffs on your e-cigarette every day.

For those who started vaping without having previously smoked, one or more of the other reasons in the list will probably apply.

b) I suppose it's just a habit

Habit is not the reason you vape.

If it were so, you could easily give it up or change it. This is one of the excuses vapers use because they don't really understand why they vape. Or they may just say 'habit' when asked why they do it because it's a common idea and they haven't given it much thought.

c) **For the hand-to-mouth gesture**

This is the only part vaping that one could call a habit: it mimics the action of smoking and this may seem one of its attractions. But please keep in mind that you want to be rid of vaping and its associated habits – or you wouldn't be reading this book. Therefore you can be glad that very soon you won't be making this tic-like gesture all day!

d) **I'm only a social vaper / I only vape with a drink**

These are what I call the *imonly* and *ionly* vapers, respectively. It makes not the slightest difference whether you're an *imonly* or an *ionly* or just an ordinary vaper. There are only two things you can be with regard to vaping: either you do it, or you don't.

The *ionly* or *imonly* kind of response is given, perhaps unthinkingly, as an excuse or justification for vaping.

e) **Stress relief**

Other things being equal, who has more stress: someone who vapes or someone who doesn't vape (or smoke)?

Nicotine isn't a tranquilliser – it's a stimulant. If you put nicotine into your body by vaping or any other means your pulse and blood pressure will go up.

Vapers are in a stressed state all the time, although they may feel better immediately after having inhaled several puffs on their e-cigarette.

It's the temporary relief of this nicotine-induced stress by another dose of the poison nicotine that creates the illusion that vaping calms you down.

In reality, vaping does not and cannot help relieve the stress of life's normal difficulties and disappointments.

f) Enjoyment

What, exactly, is enjoyable about repeatedly sucking a nicotine-laced aerosol into your mouth and lungs? Do you experience some real pleasure when you do this? Do you really take hundreds of puffs on your e-cigarette every day because you *enjoy* it? Or is it, perhaps, that you enjoy the synthetic chemical flavour which is added to the nicotine-laced aerosol?

If you say 'enjoyment' as a reason for vaping, it doesn't make sense. The clue to this is that you feel a strong need to do it repeatedly every day. There is no other enjoyable human activity I can think of which you need to indulge in so frequently and which makes you feel uncomfortable or irritable if you can't do it.

It will become clear as we proceed that the so-called enjoyment of vaping is an illusion; it's not the reason you vape.

g) **I love the taste and there are so many wonderful flavours to choose from!**

This makes no sense.

If your mouth and teeth are in a normal healthy state, between meals (or when not drinking tea or coffee), you'll have no discernible taste in your mouth. Indeed, the sensation of an unusual taste is a reason people can have for consulting a doctor: it's called dysgeusia. Besides, if you have a yearning for banana or vanilla custard flavour, you can eat a banana or some vanilla custard!

Flavoured vape juice is a marketing gimmick. Why would you want the frequently repeated experience every day of an artificial taste on your tongue and smell in your nose? It's abnormal, and if you think about it, probably not very pleasant.

Look at people vaping. Are they having such a wonderful time?

At frequent intervals they take a puff on their e-cigarette – *the device hardly ever leaves their hand* – and then they blow the vapour out again! Is this really because they want to experience some wonderful flavour?

h) Relieves boredom

Vapers may say this, but is it true?

Observe people vaping outside an office building. They're taking a few minutes' break, being forced to interrupt what they were doing before, to stand in the open, rain or shine, to top up their nicotine levels. *Doing this is boring*. That's why you may see people with an e-cigarette in one hand and their phone in the other: it helps to pass the time while they inhale more nicotine.

The same applies if you have to go into a designated smoking or vaping area to puff away on your e-cigarette.

Apart from this, is your life really so bland and empty that you need to vape as a kind of hobby to relieve the tedium of everyday existence? More likely, you find there aren't enough hours in the day for everything you want to do.

A little thought will show that boredom as a reason for vaping makes no sense. One of my patients put it like this: 'Vaping occupies and wastes time.'

i) **Something to do with my hands**

You've got to be joking! In any case, you only use one hand to vape.

Why not fiddle with a pen, squeeze a stress ball, or just clasp your hands in front of you?

And how do non-smokers manage?

j) **Lets me to take a break**

Why can't you take a break without vaping? And how come you need so many breaks anyway?

More likely, rather than vaping helping you to take a break, *you take a break in order to vape.*

k) **Helps concentration**

Vaping may seem to help concentration, but this is another illusion. I'll explain why in the section dealing with nicotine withdrawal.

Please think about why it seems difficult to concentrate *without* nicotine.

And again, how do non-vapers and non-smokers manage?

l) Weight control

Vaping, through nicotine acting on your brain, may reduce one's appetite, but there are plenty of fat people who vape and many thin people who don't, so it's not a reliable way to control your weight.

Sometimes vapers say they're afraid to stop because they'll put on weight, but it's not the absence of nicotine that makes people fat.

Rather, to mention fear of weight gain as a reason for vaping is because many nicotine users don't really want to quit, so they seize on this idea as an excuse to carry on vaping.

In reality, if you stop vaping and all nicotine use, with your new-found sense of well-being and pride that you've overcome nicotine addiction, you'll find it's not too difficult to use a little discipline to eat in a healthy way to control your weight.

m) Blowing clouds is a cool new hobby

You might have thought it was cool when you started vaping, but does it still really make you look cool? Producing clouds of vapour is more like a child blowing soap bubbles.

I trust by now you'll realise that this does not explain your apparent need to puff on your e-cigarette hundreds of times every day.

n) **It's fun to vape with my friends**

If anything, vaping interferes with social life since more and more people these days don't like to be around vapers or smokers.

The reality is that you probably feel *less foolish* about vaping if you're doing it with other people who have also failed to quit.

And what about non-vapers and non-smokers? Don't they have a social life?

o) **Nicotine addiction**

Correct!

For the practical purpose of quitting vaping and regaining *freedom from addiction,* you need to understand that this is the *only* reason you vape.

If you came to vaping as a way of quitting smoking you'll be only too well aware that all you have achieved is that you're now addicted to vaping.

Whether vaping is safer, let alone 95 per cent safer, than smoking isn't really the point. You don't want to have to vape, that is, take hundreds of puffs on your e-cigarette every day for the rest of your life, because this is what you're facing – unless you quit.

Similarly, if you came to vaping without previously being a smoker, you're in the same situation: you've become addicted to the nicotine in the e-cigarette aerosol and are puffing away repeatedly.

p) It takes away the need to vape – until I want to do it again!

This is the essence of nicotine addiction.

We'll say more about it later.

4. Why do you want to quit vaping?

Your list will probably include one or more of the following:

- **Fed up** with having to vape all the time

- **Health risks** could emerge as a result of vaping every day for years on end

- **Nuisance** having to keep buying supplies of e-liquid and keeping the device charged up

- **Bad example** to children

- **Inconvenient** as more and more public places are non-vaping and non-smoking, and I always have to carry my e-cigarette around

- **Environmental pollution** with disposable vapes is an important concern

- **Waste of money** to buy endless supplies of e-liquid and other vaping paraphernalia

- **Self-conscious** of going about sucking on an e-cigarette. Sometimes I feel a right Charlie[8] doing this.

- **Higher life insurance premiums.** Vapers are often regarded as being in the same category as smokers for life insurance purposes.

- **I want to be free from nicotine addiction!**

- **All of the above**

[8] British slang for a silly or foolish person.

If we compare, on the one hand, the reasons you have for vaping, and on the other hand, the important motives you have for wanting to stop inhaling a nicotine-laced aerosol all day, it's unarguable that the only sensible thing to do is – just quit!

So why don't you?

The answer is that vaping is not much to do with logic but everything to do with nicotine addiction. I shall discuss this in detail soon.

Crucial part of the 'Understanding' step

5. What do you actually feel when you want to take another puff on your e-cigarette?

The answer to this question is the key to successful quitting.

It's importand that you've written down your answer before reading further.

It will probably include one or more of the following:

- Nothing
- Don't know
- I feel like I want to vape, or go back to smoking!
- Mildly anxious
- Slightly irritable or short-tempered

- Distracted and have difficulty concentrating
- Feel as if something is missing

If you've used the scoring system suggested above, it's unlikely you'll have recorded anything more than a '2' in terms of severity.

Stopping vaping is like stopping smoking in that your aim – a wonderful aim! – is to stop putting nicotine into your body. And never to start again.

You may, therefore, be prone to experience, insofar as you experience anything at all, nicotine withdrawal symptoms.

If you Google 'nicotine withdrawal' or 'smoking withdrawal' you'll get *millions* of results. Long lists are trotted out of awful symptoms you might suffer if you quit nicotine, such as stomach upsets, depression, sleeping difficulties, cough, dizziness, headaches, and 'cravings'.

The good news, however, is that *these are all grossly exaggerated or untrue.* The vast majority of people I've helped to quit nicotine don't mention such symptoms.

What they do mention, when they become aware of the need for more nicotine, is mild anxiety, irritability, or distraction.

Alleged difficulties of quitting

Why, then, are so many alleged unpleasant withdrawal symptoms trotted out on the internet and in journal articles as if they're gospel truths?

The main reason is because of the way research on smoking withdrawal (nicotine withdrawal) is conducted: with questionnaires and box-ticking methods.

Being confronted with a list of suggested answers implies that these are, indeed, symptoms that nicotine users might experience. They may then be influenced to tick the boxes without giving them much thought:

> *The following is a list of nicotine withdrawal symptoms. Check all that apply to you: cravings, headaches, stomach pains, depression, nervousness, sleeping difficulties,* etc.

Instead of this, I asked you the open-ended question above: what do you actually feel when you want to take another puff on your e-cigarette?

What answer did you write down?

Why you get nicotine withdrawal symptoms

As soon as you start inhaling from your e-cigarette, nicotine is absorbed from your lungs into the bloodstream and carried to your brain.

You keep inhaling until you feel satisfied or comfortable. At this point you have achieved the level of nicotine that your brain has got used to.

It's important to realise that you're then in an altered mental state or drugged state.

If you put nicotine into your bloodstream the body's detoxifying (cleansing) mechanisms will go into action to get rid of it. It's eliminated mainly in the urine.

Thus, your nicotine level starts to fall shortly after you stop puffing on your e-cigarette. You may, therefore, after a little while start to feel something: the dreaded cravings and other withdrawal symptoms are coming upon you!

But what do you actually feel?

Fear of quitting vaping

You need to ask yourself: Will the feelings I notice when I stop vaping ever become severe or intolerable?

The answer is that this will only happen if you think it will happen!

The reality is that such withdrawal symptoms as you do feel are mild. They may be noticeable but they're *not that bad*.

For the great majority of vapers, when they become aware of the feeling that they need another puff on their e-cigarette, what they're actually experiencing is mild anxiety, irritability, or distraction. There is no physical pain.

It should be noted that some vapers don't even have these. All they are aware of is the feeling that they want to vape – but this is *only an idea in the mind.*

What vapers or other nicotine users do *not* say is that they have a headache coming on as if they're a migraine sufferer, they get pains in their stomach, their sleep is disturbed, they feel depressed, or that they're afflicted by cravings!

If someone really suffered like this they would be ill and in need of medical attention. Or if they felt seriously depressed they would be in a bad way and probably dread the start of each day.

Does the absence of nicotine cause depression? If you think it does, it follows that you're condemned to use nicotine for the rest of your life.

This is an excuse vapers may make to themselves, because, as with all addictions, in a sense they don't *want* to stop and therefore take the position that they *can't* stop.

In such a case, vapers would have a choice: top up their nicotine levels as soon as possible or grit their teeth and *endure* the symptoms for days, weeks, or even months until they would at last go away. But people have busy lives and may say they haven't the time or can't face riding out the withdrawal symptoms, so it's simpler to carry on indefinitely putting nicotine into their body.

Whatever it is that you feel, you interpret it, correctly in a sense, to mean that you need more nicotine.

Non-nicotine users don't have this problem; they just go about their daily lives. But as a vaper you're not comfortable until you've had another dose of nicotine. And as I've already mentioned but it's worth repeating: *if you put nicotine into your body, in any form, you'll want to go on putting nicotine into your body.*

How to handle withdrawal symptoms

Why do withdrawal symptoms happen? It's your body's way of reacting to the lack of nicotine and may take a little getting used to.

If you view the prospect of being nicotine-free with joyful anticipation, you can say to yourself:

I'm so glad that the last vestiges of nicotine are being cleansed from my body! This is how it feels as I'm adjusting to being nicotine-free. From now on, I'm never going to poison myself with nicotine again!

The important point is not to worry if you feel slightly uncomfortable.

You have to face the reality that either you stop vaping right now and forevermore, or you continue to vape (or put nicotine into your body in some other way) *for the rest of your life.*

It's essential to keep in mind that *it's marvellous to be nicotine-free* and return to the normal undrugged state.

This is an entirely different situation from trying to quit nicotine by willpower to force yourself not to vape in spite of feeling you want to. With such an approach you may well be setting yourself up for failure. (The same applies to smoking or other ways of putting nicotine into your body.)

If you follow what I have set out above, quitting vaping without a struggle can be within your grasp. This is because you'll approach the problem with the right attitude based on understanding, instead of using brute force.

Fear of relapsing to smoking

If you started vaping as a way of stopping smoking you may be afraid that if you stop vaping you'll be driven back to smoking.

Similarly, if you didn't previously smoke, you may want to try smoking as a substitute for vaping.

Please keep in mind that the object is not just to stop vaping: it's to become *nicotine-free.*

'Flip the switch'

It's not uncommon for vapers or smokers to wake up one morning and realise they've had enough of poisoning themselves with nicotine: they just don't want to do it anymore. So they don't. It's as if a switch had flipped in their brain.

With the Symonds Method, as explained above, you can learn how to 'flip the switch' by changing your attitude, so that you won't *want* to vape (or smoke) again. So you won't.

One word of caution: you need to be mindful not to start thinking about vaping (or other forms of nicotine use) in the old, wrong way. This is because in an unguarded moment you might find yourself tempted to vape (or smoke) again.

The key to this situation is in the word 'temptation'. No one in their right mind would be tempted to vape or smoke. So if you should ever in the future find yourself tempted, you need ask yourself:

> **Do I want to remain drug-free for the rest of my life – or do I want to be a drug (nicotine) addict again?**

Instruction

The obvious - indeed, the only - way to stop the vicious cycle of nicotine withdrawal symptoms followed by short-lived relief through taking more puffs on your e-cigarette followed again by withdrawal symptoms is

STOP PUTTING NICOTINE INTO YOUR BODY!

Unless you do this, you'll remain in the unfortunate situation where every time you puff on your e-cigarette, you will reinforce the need to keep doing it.

You must hold it clearly in mind that if you have that next puff, inevitably and necessarily, you'll want another. And another...

But if you stop putting nicotine into your body - just like that - what about withdrawal symptoms?

It's understandable to be concerned about this. But we've already noted that the withdrawal symptoms are nothing more than mild anxiety, irritability, or distraction. There is no actual pain.

Also as noted above, you might *be afraid* these symptoms will become severe or intolerable. Many people believe that you'll be chewing the wall or climbing the carpet. (Or is it the other way round?)

There are even clichés about this: 'My nerves will be shot to pieces,' or 'I'll be hell to live with,' and unkind jokes: 'Oh, the pangs, the pangs!'

The reality is: THIS IS NOT TRUE!

It's essential to develop a new attitude based on what actually happens (if anything) when you cease vaping, and to put aside all the misinformation and illusions so many people believe.

If you do this you'll realise

THERE IS NOTHING TO GIVE UP EXCEPT THE FEAR OF NOT VAPING

By keeping this in mind you'll be able to replace the fear of not vaping with the truth that

IT'S WONDERFUL TO BE NICOTINE-FREE!

You may also be afraid that if you stop vaping you'll lose something important: the pleasure it gives you, or the way it helps you to relax, or both.

It cannot be repeated too often: these ideas are illusions. Vaping is not enjoyable – it's horrible and faintly ridiculous. Nor is it helpful in any way, for example as a tranquilliser: it winds you up rather than calms you down.

Nor is it an aid to concentration: it makes concentration more difficult.

Imagine you have an important job of work, such as a report to write. Of course you need to organise your thoughts, clear your desk, and arrange your materials or sit in front of your computer.

But as a vaper, in addition to doing this, you need to make sure your e-cigarette is to hand, the battery charged up, and the device filled with e-juice. Then, you repeatedly have to bring your hand to your mouth – and suck on your e-cigarette. How can you do this and write or type if you're *distracted* by having to vape all the time?

The reality is that if you stop vaping, that is, if you stop putting the poison nicotine into your body, you'll achieve two wonderful goals:

1. **You'll no longer be in an altered mental state with nicotine all the time**

2. **You'll no longer suffer drug withdrawal symptoms**

Now let's think about what may happen if you haven't vaped for while and you become aware of the mild anxious irritable feelings.

If you don't vape again what will happen to these feelings?

Check all that apply:

- ☐ They will become intolerable
- ☐ They will be with me forever
- ☐ I will want to jump out of the window
- ☐ They will go away

You ticked the last box, did you not?

That's right: they will go away!

They will go away and never come back – *unless you put more nicotine into your body* – which, of course, from now on you'll never want to do again.

How long will it take for these feelings to go away permanently?

It usually takes three or four days, exceptionally up to a week.

After this time there will be no detectable nicotine left in your body, so how can you experience withdrawal symptoms from something that is already completely withdrawn?

Many people, with the right frame of mind based on knowledge of the reality of vaping, don't experience *any* withdrawal symptoms because they're so delighted with the idea that they can stop straightaway and permanently just by having the right attitude.

If you do become aware of withdrawal symptoms, you can tell yourself:

This is what it feels like as the last vestige of the poison nicotine is being cleansed from my body. This is marvellous! Soon these artificially caused slightly unpleasant feelings will be gone for good.

If from time to time in the next few days you do become aware of the anxious irritable feelings, DON'T LET THEM BOTHER YOU – JUST CONTINUE WITH YOUR USUAL ACTIVITIES.

You must be absolutely clear that if you do vape (or worse, smoke a cigarette) to get rid of these feelings, it's guaranteed they will come back in full force.

So, *do you want to experience these feelings for a few days (if at all) or repeatedly every day for the rest of your life?*

Another key to successfully stopping vaping is in the word 'temptation'.

If you feel tempted to vape you're thinking about it in the old, wrong way.

No one in their right mind would be tempted to inhale a nicotine aerosol.

Therefore, please adjust your attitude!

One reason for giving in to the temptation to smoke is to do with the nature of addiction: illogical though it is, you might not really want to quit.

If you recognise yourself in this position, remind yourself of the truth:

Vaping

- produces an altered mental state
- is not enjoyable
- is not relaxing
- does not relieve stress
- does not help concentration
- is utterly and completely pointless

Now ask yourself whether it's really so difficult to replace the fear of not vaping with the truth that it's great to be nicotine-free!

Time to Start Your Vape-Free Life

Quitting vaping, as I have indicated, is largely a problem of how you think about it.

Therefore, you need to acquire a new attitude. You should have been able to do this by following the steps of the Symonds Method. Let me repeat the three main points:

1. You vaped only because of nicotine addiction
2. The reason it seemed difficult to stop was because of nicotine withdrawal symptoms
3. Such withdrawal symptoms as you do experience are not that bad

I have deliberately put the first two sentences in the past tense.

The question, then, for the Time to Start, is this: are you going to do it?

Are you *right now* going to begin enjoying the rest of your life without vaping or using any kind of nicotine product ever again?

You may be thinking it can't be that simple. But the reality is that it *is* that simple!

This worry, if you have it, arises from a faint echo of the idea you used to have that you didn't really want to stop.

You need to be on your guard against such thoughts. But note: the very fact you have doubts (if you do) is an indication of the old, wrong way of thinking about nicotine use.

Your last vape

Let's consider the last puff you'll ever take on your e-cigarette device (or ever did take) in your life.

Your attitude towards and feelings about this situation are of the highest importance.

Other approaches to ceasing nicotine use tend to view this happy state as if you're saying goodbye to an old and dear friend. It's part of the problem of 'preparing' to quit and setting a 'quit date'.

Many vapers believe that vaping is enjoyable or helpful in some way, but for the sake of their health and for other good reasons such as saving money, they know it's only sensible to say goodbye to vaping.

If you approach quitting in this way, with regrets and doubts, it's likely you'll also experience the dreaded 'urges' or 'cravings' to vape again and, worst of all, you'll suffer awful withdrawal symptoms!

I've already explained why this is wrong, but here I'll use only three words: *Nonsense! Rubbish! Untrue!*

You're not going to say Goodbye to vaping.

You're going to say *Good riddance!*

Nicotine, delivered by vaping or another means is NOT your friend, crutch, pleasure, stress reliever, aid to concentration, or enhancer of social situations.

(If you think it is, then please re-read the section 'Why do you vape now?')

Therefore, it's of the greatest importance that you stop vaping (and all nicotine use) *right now*. Don't put it off till the 'right time' – it will never be the right time.

And don't think of putting it off till the happy day when you have less stress – as a vaper you're *always* stressed.

If you have a half-finished pod or tank of e-liquid, disposing of it responsibly is an important symbolic – indeed liberating – act: you don't *need* nicotine anymore!

Let me remind you: there are only two stages in ceasing nicotine use.

One is stopping; the other is staying stopped.

The art of staying stopped, therefore, is to know what to do if you feel tempted to vape again.

We've already discussed this but I would like to share with you the following ideas that I have found helpful for those vapers who may still have difficulty.

As always, understanding is the key to the problem.

Let's consider what happens as time goes by after you've taken your last puff on your e-cigarette.

What happens after you stop vaping

Four hours

What's likely to happen in the first four (or a few) hours after your last vape?

The short answer is nothing. Or you'll probably be feeling excited at the prospect of stopping vaping easily.

Many of my patients, having gained a proper understanding of why they used to vape, find it's easy to ignore such desires as they may have to vape again in the next few days.

If the idea that you want to vape is more persistent, ask yourself what it amounts to.

The answer is that it's nothing worse than mild anxiety or a vague feeling that something is missing. *These are only ideas in your mind.*

There is no cause for worry or alarm.

Just take note that this is how you feel and remind yourself it's due to the nicotine being cleansed from your body.

Be happy about it!

Don't worry that these feelings may become severe or intolerable. They won't.

It's most important just to carry on with whatever you were doing when you became aware of the idea that you wanted to vape.

You don't need to *do* anything about it, such as eating a healthy snack, drinking a glass of water, taking deep breaths, or distracting yourself – this is giving it far too much importance!

The feeling or idea that you want to vape will go away naturally.

Four months

Some of the same feelings may recur from time to time in the next few months after your last vape and you can deal with them in the same way.

As time goes by you'll have longer and longer periods without thinking about vaping and eventually you'll probably forget about it altogether.

Other methods of stopping nicotine use will tell you to be aware of 'triggers' and to avoid them if possible.

This is pointless and unnecessary.

You didn't vape in the past because of triggers, but as I hardly need remind you, because of nicotine withdrawal symptoms.

If one of the so-called triggers was having a cup of coffee, what are you supposed to do – give up coffee?

If you carry on normally (apart from vaping, of course) you may well find you're not drinking so much coffee as you used to, and this is probably better for your health.

The fact that you've stopped vaping is no reason to change anything else in your life, unless you want to.

Forever!

This is the happy state you were in before you started vaping or smoking and that non-nicotine users are in all the time, other things being equal.

You're infinitely better off – can there be ever the slightest doubt about it? – with *freedom from nicotine addiction.*

Why, then, do some vapers even years after quitting still yearn for a vape or a smoke?

It's because they've quit through willpower and are forcing themselves not to vape or smoke even though they think they need or would enjoy it.

This is due to misperceptions about nicotine use. It's explained above in the section dealing with the idea that vaping may seem enjoyable or useful in relieving stress.

Coping with difficulties without vaping

Some people who have recently stopped vaping find (or think they find) they can't cope with the normal difficulties and stresses of everyday life; they blame this on the absence of vaping and use it as an excuse to start doing it again.

For example, if you've had an argument with someone or your computer has crashed, you would feel annoyed and unhappy.

In your vaping days the first thing you would probably do would be to reach for your e-cigarette, if you weren't already using it, because it *seemed* to make you feel better. Why was this?

You'll remember it's because, as a vaper, you were already in a slightly stressed state due to nicotine withdrawal; you had a few more puffs and overall you felt better.

All that this achieved was merely to relieve the mild stress caused by nicotine withdrawal; the external situation was unchanged.

Therefore, you had the understandable but mistaken idea that vaping relieves stress. It doesn't.

It should help to keep in mind that, as a non-nicotine user, you'll be able to deal with the normal difficulties of life *better* than before because you won't have the stress of nicotine withdrawal all the time *in addition*.

Similarly, you'll be able to concentrate better on whatever you have to do because you won't suffer the almost constant distraction of mild nicotine withdrawal symptoms!

Vape-free socialising

Another situation for which you need to be on your guard is meeting other vapers or smokers. This may happen in one of the diminishing number of public places where vaping or smoking is allowed, or at a private party.

If you see someone vaping what will you think? How much fun that is? You wish you could do it without feeling guilty? That you can't enjoy the party without nicotine?

Even if you're having a drink at home and no one else objects to exhaled e-cigarette vapour, are you really missing something if you don't vape?

Previously, in social situations you may have felt more at ease by vaping or smoking, but only because immediately before you vaped or smoked you were not at ease due to nicotine withdrawal.

Vapers are never fully at ease, except they may think they are for a short time immediately after having taken a few puffs.

You'll remember this is an illusion because you were then in a mildly altered mental state. So don't make the mistake of thinking smoking will make social situations more enjoyable. It won't.

Facing the new reality of being nicotine-free!

So, what do you want to do? Cease vaping for good or carry on vaping for the rest of your life?

As the Americans would say with their colourful use of English, this is a no-brainer. You *can't* have the occasional vape: it's all or nothing.

If you don't believe this, see what happens if you stop vaping for a week and then take a few puffs on your e-cigarette.

It's almost inevitable you'll immediately want to resume vaping repeatedly throughout the day.

In any case, why would anyone in their right mind want suck a nicotine-laden aerosol into their lungs at all, even once?

It represents the old, wrong way of thinking about vaping: that it's enjoyable or helpful somehow in relieving stress. As we have noted, *these ideas are illusions*.

It's my hope and belief that when you've worked through this book you'll never again think about vaping in the old way.

When non-nicotine users leave their home they never have to check that they have an e-cigarette in their pocket or handbag.

The main difference, however, between someone who's never vaped or smoked and someone who's used the Symonds Method of quitting, is that you need to be on your guard not to fall into the trap of thinking about vaping or smoking again in the old, wrong way!

If you can do this, from now on you'll be able to

ENJOY YOUR FREEDOM FROM NICOTINE ADDICTION!

***

Readers are welcome to contact Dr Symonds by email with any questions or comments:
info@nicotinemonkey.com

Numerous interesting blog posts about smoking, vaping, and other medical matters can be found on Dr Symonds's website:
https://www.nicotinemonkey.com/blog/

Nicotine
Monkey

Printed in Great Britain
by Amazon